Theory Paper   Grade 7   2015   A

Duration 3 hours

Candidates should answer all FIVE questions.
Write your answers on this paper – no others will be accepted.
Answers must be written clearly and neatly – otherwise marks may be lost.

TOTAL MARKS
100

1 Indicate suitable chords for a continuo player by figuring the bass as necessary, *from the beginning of bar 2*, at the places marked ∗ in this passage. If you wish to use a $\frac{5}{3}$ chord leave the space under the asterisk blank, but $\frac{5}{3}$ chords *must* be shown when used as part of a $\frac{6}{4}\frac{5}{3}$ progression or when chromatic alteration is required. All other chords should be indicated (including repeated accidentals within the same bar), as should any suspended dissonances.

J. S. Bach, Suite in C minor, BWV 997 (adapted)

3

2 On the staves marked **A** below is an outline of a passage adapted from a piano piece by Haydn, leaving out certain passing notes and other notes of melodic decoration. The music on the staves marked **B** is what the composer actually wrote. Continuing in the same style, reconstruct the blank and partially completed bars. Note that the left-hand part starts in the treble clef.

etc.

Music Theory Past Papers 2015

ABRSM Grade 7

3 EITHER

(a) Complete the clarinet part (at concert pitch) in the following passage, which is adapted from a song by Fauré. Phrase marks have been inserted above the clarinet stave to indicate the structure you might use.

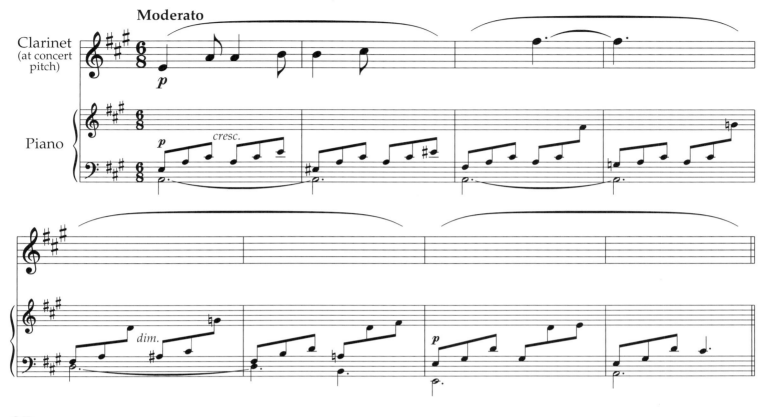

OR

(b) Compose a complete melody of not less than eight bars in length for unaccompanied flute or violin, based on the given opening. Write the complete melody on the staves below, include appropriate performance directions for the instrument of your choice and state which it is.

Instrument ....

4 Look at the extract printed opposite, which is from a song, and then answer the questions below.

(a) Give the meaning of **Bewegt**. .... (2)

(b) Identify the chords marked ✳ in bars 8 (shaded) and 15 by writing on the dotted lines below. Use either words or symbols. Indicate the position of each chord, show whether it is major, minor, augmented or diminished, and name the prevailing key in bar 8.

Bar 8 .... Key .... (4)

Bar 15 .... (3)

(c) Name four features of the music that contribute to the change of mood in bars 20–21.

1 .... (1)

2 .... (1)

3 .... (1)

4 .... (1)

(d) Complete the following statements:

(i) The first bar in which the soprano sounds at a lower
pitch than the top line of the right-hand piano part is bar .... (2)

(ii) There is an upward-resolving appoggiatura in the soprano part in bar .... (2)

(e) Mark **clearly** on the score, using the appropriate capital letter for identification, one example of each of the following. Also give the bar number of each of your answers. The first answer is given.

In bars 10–20

A a dominant 7th chord in third inversion (V7d)
in the tonic key (mark Ⓐ above the notes). Bar ..16....

B a rising chromatic semitone (augmented unison)
in the right-hand piano part (circle the notes concerned). Bar(s) .... (2)

C a harmonic interval of a compound diminished 8ve between the
soprano part and the left-hand piano part (circle the notes concerned). Bar .... (2)

D a melodic interval of a diminished 5th in
the soprano part (circle the notes concerned). Bar(s) .... (2)

(f) From the list below, underline the name of the most likely composer of this piece and give a reason for your choice.

Chopin   Bach   Verdi   Schumann (1)

Reason:

.... (1)

5 Look at the extract printed on pages 9–10, which is from Ravel's *Valses nobles et sentimentales*, and then answer the questions below.

(a) Give the meaning of:

à 2 (e.g. bar 5, flutes)   .... (2)

Cédez (bar 6)   .... (2)

gliss. (bar 7, second harp)   .... (2)

(b) (i) Write out the parts for first and second horns in bars 1–3 as they would sound at concert pitch.

Horns

(3)

(ii) Using the blank stave at the foot of page 10, write out the parts for clarinets in bars 7–8 as they would sound at concert pitch. (4)

(c) Complete the following statements:

(i) On the first note of bar 2, the instruments *sounding* an octave higher than the double

basses are the .... and the .... (2)

(ii) On the first beat of bar 3, the instruments *sounding* in unison with the upper note of the

cellos are the .... and the .... (2)

(d) Mark **clearly** on the score, using the appropriate capital letter for identification, one example of each of the following. Also give the bar number(s) of each of your answers. The first answer is given.

A   an instruction to play suddenly quiet.   Bar ....¹....

B   an augmented chord in the first harp part (circle the notes concerned).   Bar .... (2)

C   a melodic interval of a minor 7th in the
viola part (circle the notes concerned).   Bar .... (2)

D   two consecutive harmonic intervals of a major 3rd
between the first and second flutes (circle the notes concerned).   Bar .... (2)

(e) Answer TRUE or FALSE to the following statement:

The first flute and first oboe sound in unison throughout bars 1–7.   .... (2)

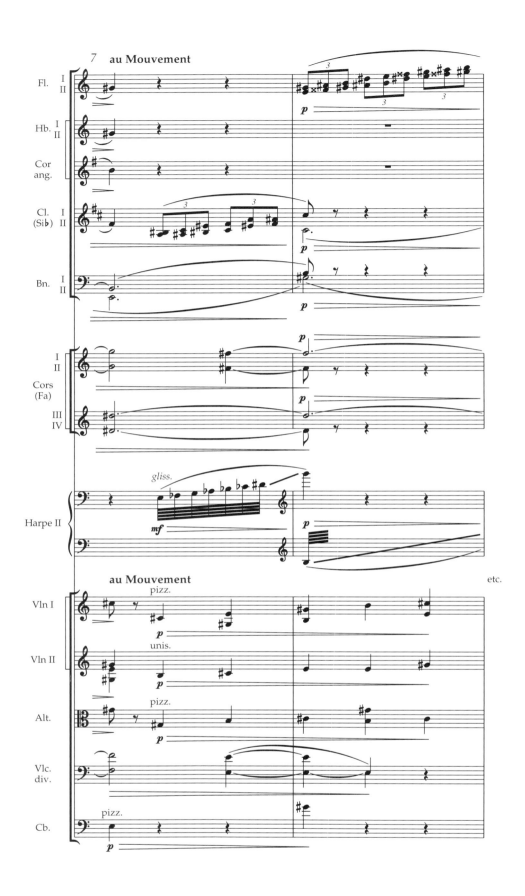

(b) (ii)

bars 7–8

Clarinets 1 2

Theory Paper   Grade 7   2015   B

Duration 3 hours

Candidates should answer all FIVE questions.
Write your answers on this paper – no others will be accepted.
Answers must be written clearly and neatly – otherwise marks may be lost.

TOTAL MARKS
100

1 Indicate suitable chords for a continuo player by figuring the bass as necessary, *from the beginning of bar 3*, at the places marked ∗ in this passage. If you wish to use a $\frac{5}{3}$ chord leave the space under the asterisk blank, but $\frac{5}{3}$ chords *must* be shown when used as part of a $\frac{6}{4}\frac{5}{3}$ progression or when chromatic alteration is required. All other chords should be indicated (including repeated accidentals within the same bar), as should any suspended dissonances.

15

2 On the staves marked **A** below is an outline of a passage adapted from a chorale harmonized by J. S. Bach, leaving out certain suspensions, passing notes and other notes of melodic decoration. The music on the staves marked **B** is what the composer actually wrote. Continuing in the same style, reconstruct the blank and partially completed bars.

3 EITHER

(a) Complete the violin part in the following passage, which is adapted from a piece by Dancla. Phrase marks have been inserted above the violin stave to indicate the structure you might use.

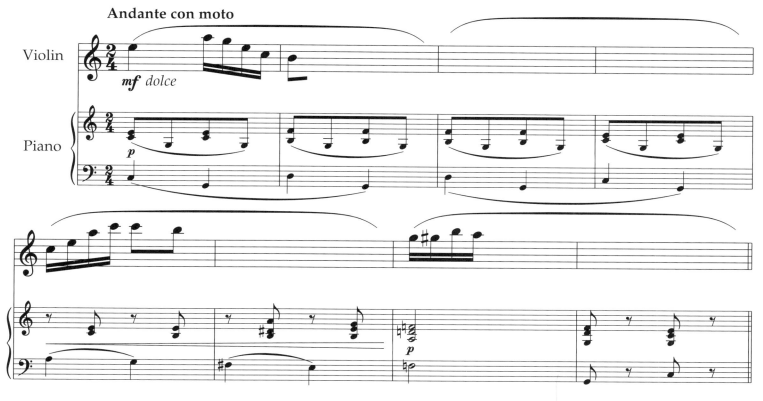

OR

(b) Compose a complete melody of eight bars in length for unaccompanied oboe or trumpet (at concert pitch). Form your melody from the chord progression below, using the chords for each bar, together with any diatonic or chromatic decorations you consider appropriate. You may use the given opening or not, as you prefer. Write the complete melody on the staves below, include appropriate performance directions for the instrument of your choice and state which it is.

Instrument ....

Adagio con molta espressione

etc.

4 Look at the extract printed opposite, which is from a piano sonata, and then answer the questions below.

(a) Identify the chords marked * in bars 3 and 5 (shaded) by writing on the dotted lines below. Use either words or symbols. Indicate the position of each chord, show whether it is major, minor, augmented or diminished, and name the prevailing key in bar 5.

Bar 3 .... (3)

Bar 5 .... Key .... (4)

(b) Write out in full the right-hand part of bar 8 as you think it should be played.

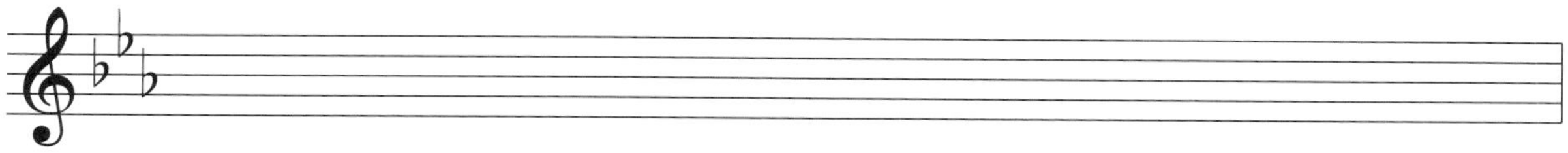

(5)

(c) Mark **clearly** on the score, using the appropriate capital letter for identification, one example of each of the following. Also give the bar number(s) of each of your answers. The first answer is given.

In bars 1–10

A   an instruction to play the notes slightly separated.   Bar ....3....

B   a pedal note lasting for at least four bars (mark └───B───┘ under the bars).   Bars .... (2)

C   a harmonic interval of a major 7th in
   the right-hand part (circle the notes concerned).   Bar .... (2)

From bar 10 onwards

D   a melodic interval of an augmented 2nd in the top line
   of the right-hand part (circle the notes concerned).   Bar .... (2)

E   simultaneous lower auxiliary notes a minor 10th apart between
   the right-hand and left-hand parts (circle the notes concerned).   Bar .... (2)

F   a bar which is a repetition (not exact) of the previous bar but an octave lower.   Bar .... (2)

(d) From the list below, underline the name of the most likely composer of this piece and give two reasons for your choice.

Handel   Chopin   Debussy   Beethoven   (1)

Reasons:

1 .... (1)

2 .... (1)

5 Look at the extract printed on pages 17–18, which is from the first movement of Nielsen's
Symphony No. 2, and then answer the questions below.

[25]

(a) Give the meaning of:

♪ (e.g. bar 1, violas) .... (2)

espress. (*espressivo*) (bar 3, 1st oboe) .... (1)

(b) (i) Write out the parts for horns in bars 1–3 as they would sound at concert pitch and using
the given clefs.

(4)

(ii) Using the blank stave at the foot of page 18, write out the part for first clarinet in bars
8–11 as it would sound at concert pitch. (4)

(c) Mark **clearly** on the score, using the appropriate capital letter for identification, one example
of each of the following. Also give the bar number(s) of each of your answers. The first answer
is given.

In the string parts

A a descending four-note chromatic figure (mark ⌊___A___⌋ under the notes). Bars ....3–5....

B a double stop that forms an interval of a minor 6th (circle the notes concerned). Bar .... (2)

C a place where the cellos have to use an open string (circle the note concerned). Bar .... (2)

(d) Describe fully the numbered and bracketed harmonic intervals *sounding* between:

1 cellos and first trombone, bar 1 .... (2)

2 violas and first horn, bar 5 .... (2)

(e) Answer TRUE or FALSE to each of the following statements:

(i) In bar 7, the second clarinet and violas *sound* an octave apart. .... (2)

(ii) From bar 7 onwards, the cellos and first bassoon sound in unison. .... (2)

(iii) In bar 2, the timpanist is instructed to retune the timpani to B and F♯. .... (2)

(b) (ii)

bars 8–11

Clarinet 1

Theory Paper   Grade 7   2015   C

Duration 3 hours

Candidates should answer all FIVE questions.
Write your answers on this paper – no others will be accepted.
Answers must be written clearly and neatly – otherwise marks may be lost.

TOTAL MARKS
100

1 Indicate suitable chords for a continuo player by figuring the bass as necessary, *from the third beat of bar 2*, at the places marked ∗ in this passage. If you wish to use a $\frac{5}{3}$ chord leave the space under the asterisk blank, but $\frac{5}{3}$ chords *must* be shown when used as part of a $\frac{6}{4}\frac{5}{3}$ progression or when chromatic alteration is required. All other chords should be indicated (including repeated accidentals within the same bar), as should any suspended dissonances.

15

Handel, Sonata in A, HWV 372 (adapted)

2 On the staves marked **A** below is an outline of a passage adapted from a chorale harmonized by J. S. Bach, leaving out certain suspensions, passing notes and other notes of melodic decoration. The music on the staves marked **B** is what the composer actually wrote. Continuing in the same style, reconstruct the blank and partially completed bars.

3 EITHER

(a) Complete the bassoon part in the following passage, which is adapted from a piece by Milde. Phrase marks have been inserted above the bassoon stave to indicate the structure you might use.

OR

(b) Compose a complete melody of not less than eight bars in length for unaccompanied violin or flute, based on the given opening. Write the complete melody on the staves below, include appropriate performance directions for the instrument of your choice and state which it is.

Instrument ....

Un Scherzo all'antico
Allegro, ma non troppo (♩. = 60)

4 Look at the extract printed opposite, which is from Hummel's Piano Sonata No. 6, Op. 106, and then answer the questions below.

(a) Identify the chords marked * in bars 3 and 30 by writing on the dotted lines below. Use either words or symbols. Indicate the position of each chord, show whether it is major, minor, augmented or diminished, and name the prevailing key.

Bar 3 .... Key .... (4)

Bar 30 .... Key .... (4)

(b) Write out in full the top right-hand part of bar 11 as you think it should be played.

(3)

(c) Mark **clearly** on the score, using the appropriate capital letter for identification, one example of each of the following. Also give the bar number(s) of each of your answers. The first answer is given.

In bars 1–12 of the left-hand part

A a bar in which all the harmonic intervals are a minor 3rd.   Bar ...10...

B a dominant 7th chord in third inversion (V7d)
in the relative major key (circle the notes concerned).   Bar .... (2)

C a pedal note lasting for five beats (mark └────C────┘ under the notes).   Bars .... (2)

From bar 18 onwards in the right-hand part

D a melodic interval of a diminished 5th in the top line (circle the notes concerned).   Bar .... (2)

E a rising chromatic semitone (augmented unison)
in the inner part (circle the notes concerned).   Bar .... (2)

(d) Complete the following statements:

(i) The opening motif (marked ⌐￣￣￣⌐), played in octaves in
the left-hand part, is repeated twice at the same pitch in bars .... and bars .... (2)

(ii) The only complete bars in which the rhythm ♪. ♪ does *not* occur are bar .... and bar .... (2)

(iii) The letter name of the highest note in the right-hand part is .... and it is played in bar .... (2)

23

5 Look at the extract printed on pages 25–6, which is from a song cycle for voice and orchestra, and then answer the questions below.

(a) Give the meaning of:

Grosse Trommel   ....   (2)

Becken   ....   (2)

morendo (bar 5, flutes)   ....   (2)

Langsam (bar 7)   ....   (2)

(b) (i)   Write out the parts for horns in bar 3 as they would sound at concert pitch.

(2)

(ii)   Using the blank stave at the foot of page 26, write out the parts for clarinets in bars 7–8 as they would sound at concert pitch.   (4)

(c) Complete the following statements:

(i)   In bar 2, the highest-sounding note is played by the ....

and the ....   (2)

(ii)   The tenor voice and second horn *sound* a note in unison in bar(s) ....   (2)

(iii) There is an indication to use an up-bow in bar ....   (2)

(d) Describe fully the numbered and bracketed harmonic intervals *sounding* between:

1   first violins and second clarinet, bar 1   ....   (2)

2   violas and oboes, bar 2   ....   (2)

(e) From the list below, underline the name of the most likely composer of this piece.

Debussy   Verdi   Mahler   Stravinsky   (1)

(b) (ii)

bars 7–8

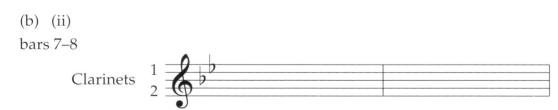

Theory Paper   Grade 7   2015   S

Duration 3 hours

Candidates should answer all FIVE questions.
Write your answers on this paper – no others will be accepted.
Answers must be written clearly and neatly – otherwise marks may be lost.

TOTAL MARKS
100

1   Indicate suitable chords for a continuo player by figuring the bass as necessary, *from the third beat of bar 2*, at the places marked * in this passage. If you wish to use a $\frac{5}{3}$ chord leave the space under the asterisk blank, but $\frac{5}{3}$ chords *must* be shown when used as part of a $\frac{6}{4}\frac{5}{3}$ progression or when chromatic alteration is required. All other chords should be indicated (including repeated accidentals within the same bar), as should any suspended dissonances.

15

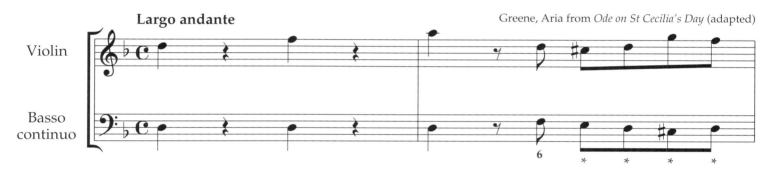

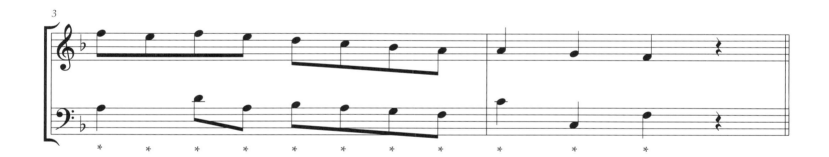

2 On the staves marked **A** below is an outline of a passage adapted from a chorale harmonized by J. S. Bach, leaving out certain suspensions, passing notes and other notes of melodic decoration. The music on the staves marked **B** is what the composer actually wrote. Continuing in the same style, reconstruct the blank and partially completed bars.

3 EITHER

(a) Complete the violin part in the following passage, which is adapted from a piece by Reger. Phrase marks have been inserted above the violin stave to indicate the structure you might use.

OR

(b) Compose a complete melody of not less than eight bars in length for unaccompanied cello or bassoon, based on the given opening. Write the complete melody on the staves below, include appropriate performance directions for the instrument of your choice and state which it is.

Instrument ....

4 Look at the extract printed opposite, which is from a violin sonata by Mozart, and then answer the questions below. [25]

(a) Identify the chords marked ∗ and shaded in bars 10 and 11 by writing on the dotted lines below. Use either words or symbols. Indicate the position of each chord and show whether it is major, minor, augmented or diminished.

Bar 10 .... ⎫ (3)
                                                                    ⎬ Key D minor
Bar 11 .... ⎭ (3)

(b) Complete the following statements:

   (i) The music begins in the key of D major. In bar 5 it passes through

   the key of .... and in bar 6 it passes through the key of .... (2)

   (ii) From bar 4 onwards, the first bar in which *all* the notes of the right-hand piano part sound at a lower pitch than the violin part is bar .... (2)

(c) Write out in full the violin part of bar 12 as you think it should be played.

(3)

(d) Mark **clearly** on the score, using the appropriate capital letter for identification, one example of each of the following. Also give the bar number of each of your answers. The first answer is given.

   In bars 1–10

   A an instruction in the violin part to play the notes slightly separated.   Bar ....9....

   B four successive notes in the right-hand piano part that form a dominant 7th chord (V7) in the tonic key (circle the notes concerned).   Bar .... (2)

   C syncopation in the right-hand piano part.   Bar .... (2)

   D a melodic interval of a diminished 5th in the violin part (circle the notes concerned).   Bar .... (2)

(e) Give the full names of the notes of melodic decoration (e.g. changing note) marked **X** and **Y** in the right-hand piano part of bars 6 and 7.

   X (bar 6)   .... (2)

   Y (bar 7)   .... (2)

(f) Answer TRUE or FALSE to the following statement:

   In bars 5–7 the left-hand piano part and the violin play the same notes an octave apart.   .... (2)

5 Look at the extract printed on pages 33–4, which is from Khachaturian's *Masquerade Suite*, and then answer the questions below.

(a) Give the meaning of:

pizz. (e.g. bar 7, cellos) .... (2)

≋
o (e.g. bar 7, violas) .... (2)

(b) (i) Write out the parts for clarinets in bar 1 as they would sound at concert pitch.

(2)

(ii) Using the blank staves at the foot of page 34, write out the parts for horns in bars 6–7 as they would sound at concert pitch. (3)

(c) Complete the following statements:

(i) On the fourth quaver of bar 6, the instruments *sounding* an octave higher than the violas

are the ...., the ...., the ....

and the .... (4)

(ii) There is an instruction for an up-bow to be used by a string section in bar .... (2)

(iii) The instrument *sounding* in unison with the
double basses on the first beat of bar 5 is the .... (2)

(iv) There is a melodic interval of an augmented 3rd in the first bassoon part in bars .... (2)

(v) There is a descending chromatic semitone
(augmented unison) in a part for a single-reed instrument in bar(s) .... (2)

(d) Describe fully the numbered and bracketed harmonic intervals *sounding* between:

1 violas and first oboe, bar 3 .... (2)

2 second violins and second clarinet, bar 4 .... (2)

(b) (ii)
bars 6–7

Horns

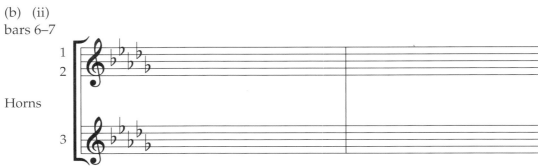